Introducing Curious Creatures

Introducing
CURIOUS CREATURES
Desmond Morris

SPRING BOOKS · LONDON

Published by

SPRING BOOKS

SPRING HOUSE · SPRING PLACE · LONDON NW5

When we are only a few years old we learn to distinguish between a cat and a dog, a horse and a cow. After another year or two we can tell the difference between a lion and a tiger, a dog and a fox, a horse and a donkey, a cow and a goat. Later still, more animal types are added to our list—the leopard, for example, the wolf, the rhino, the elephant and the antelope. The result is that when, as children, we visit the zoo for the first time, we meet a number of creatures that are already old friends from our books and stories. Nor are we particularly surprised to find that there is not just one antelope, but there are many different kinds—some big, some small, some with short horns, some with long horns, and so on. They all fit into our basic and rather vague concept of what an antelope should look like. But we also meet some new creatures at the zoo that look rather odd. They simply refuse to fit into any one of our ready-made categories, even though these categories are not very precise. Sometimes these creatures are so unusual that they demand a completely new pigeon-hole all to themselves, or else they do remind us of an old animal friend, but are strangely off-key in some way.

These creatures, the oddities of the animal world, are particularly fascinating because, with their weird and marvellous shapes and markings, they make us start to ask questions about the amazingly rich variety of animal forms which exists on the earth today. At first the unusual bumps and patterns, the bulging eyes, huge feet or protruding noses of the curious creatures strike us simply as grotesque or amusing. The pompous-looking bird reminds us of a stuffy military gentleman; or perhaps the huge rodent with protruding teeth recalls a great-aunt. But these comparisons, although they may tell us something about the pomposities of colonels or the rattiness of great-aunts, really tell us very little about unusual birds or curious rodents.

After a while, however, we begin to question the real reason for the extraordinary appearance of these creatures, and before long we have come face to face with one of the most important and basic rules of nature. This rule is that, in the competitive struggle for survival in the wild, each species must evolve a body form that is more successfully adapted than those of its rivals to deal with the problems of its particular environment. During the course of evolution, competition of this sort has often led to fantastic and extreme developments. A species with a bigger nose, for example, can smell its prey better than one with a small nose; or a species with huge claws can dig out its food more easily than one with weak claws. Where there is strong rivalry in a special habitat for a particular kind of food, there will be more and more exaggerated developments to deal with the situation.

Using this argument, it is easy to see why certain creatures have developed such enormous ears, noses, eyes, tongues, claws and teeth, but it then becomes difficult to understand why all animals have not gone to such extremes.

There are two answers to this. Firstly, there are many different ways of solving each problem. It is not vital for an animal to have a big nose or big feet, for example, to catch its prey successfully. Instead, like the snake, it may evolve its own waiting game, complete with elaborate camouflage and a special poison to incapacitate the prey. Or, like the cheetah, it may rely upon a tremendous gymnastic performance as the particular feature of its hunting.

Secondly, there is a pitfall in the path towards extreme developments—a pitfall that has extinguished thousands of species during the course of evolution. It is this.

When an animal has evolved into a highly specialised shape that gives it a supreme advantage in following a particular way of life, it is in a very secure position indeed—but only as long as its way of life remains unchanged. For instance, take the ant-eaters. These mammals have developed enormously long noses and tongues and long, curved claws for attacking termite hills and ant nests. If, for some reason, termites and ants were wiped out, the ant-eaters would all perish. They are far too specialised to be able to adapt themselves quickly to some other way of life. Other creatures that are less specialised also like to feast on termites when they can get them. Unlike the ant-eaters, they have no particular features to ensure that they can always obtain them, so they must wait for a lucky chance whenever they can. But if the termites suddenly disappeared, these unspecialised animals could quickly turn to some other source of food, such as nuts, or berries, or fruits or worms. Their bodies are all-purpose structures, ready to deal with any situation that comes along, as opposed to the highly refined body forms of the specialists of the animal world.

★   ★   ★

So far I have been giving examples of animal oddities connected with feeding behaviour, but there are other spheres of activity where the same rules are operating. Camouflage connected with self-defence also exists in very extreme forms, and once again there is the problem that if an animal specialises too much, so that its camouflage conceals it perfectly in the one particular environment, then it will never be able to leave that environment, whatever happens. If the animal has become perfectly camouflaged to look like the leaf of one species of tree, and that tree vanishes from the locality, the animal will be conspicuous wherever else it goes and will be seen and killed by its enemies. If, instead, it has only a general broken-up pattern that partially hides it on almost any sort of tree, it stands a better chance in a changing environment, but it is never quite so secure at any one moment as its more specialised rival.

On the following pages I am going to introduce you to some of the curious creatures that have, so to speak, put all their eggs in one basket in solving one problem or another. I shall also be introducing you to some other animal oddities—less specialised creatures, but ones which we find curious because they are so rare or unfamiliar to us. I trust that your encounter with them in this book will arouse your interest and curiosity in the more unusual corners of the rich complexity of the animal kingdom.

One of the weirdest looking specialists in the animal world is the scaly ant-eater, or pangolin, from Africa and Asia. Its whole appearance has been dramatically changed during the course of evolution, as the hairy coat of its ancestors has gradually developed into the hard, protective, scaly covering it is dressed in today. The pangolin is so specialised in its feeding behaviour that, unless formic acid is sprinkled over its food, it may starve to death in captivity. In the wild, its powerful claws can easily tear holes in ant or termite nests, and the insects are then gathered up on the pangolin's very long and very sticky tongue.

The armadillos of South America and southern North America have, like the pangolins, evolved a strange armoured outer covering that protects them from their enemies. It takes the form of a stiff carapace that is hinged across the middle. The number of hinges, or bands, varies from species to species, and, in the picture below, both seven-banded and nine-banded armadillos can be seen.

There is one extremely rare form, the giant armadillo (left), that is the owner of the largest claws in the animal world. It has front legs like pickaxes, elephantine back legs like huge shovels and a powerful armoured tail. It can dig a large hole faster than any other creature, hacking away with its great curved claws and shovelling the earth and stones backwards with its huge back feet.

Armadillos are scavengers as well as ant and termite eaters, but the aardvark, from Africa, is more of a specialist, eating only the insects. Like all ant-eaters, it has a long nose and strong digging claws, but it lacks the armoured protection of the other forms.

Of all the long-nosed ant-eating specialists, the one with the most impressive snout is undoubtedly the South American giant ant-eater. This creature's whole face has been pulled out into a long, thin tube that can be inserted deep into the damaged ant or termite nests.

Two other notable noses belong to the now nearly extinct solenodon (above), found in the West Indies, and the rarely seen elephant seal (below) from the Antarctic. The solenodon's long, tubular nose positively bristles with sensitive whiskers, but the elephant seal's proboscis takes the form of a bulbous, eighteen-inches-long, inflatable bladder that is enlarged when its two-ton owner becomes excited.

One glance at the tarsier, from South-east Asia, shown below, and the African bush-baby on the opposite page, tells us that their speciality lies in their enormous, sensitive eyes. These two relatives of the more familiar monkeys are leaping night-hunters. In bushes and trees they search high and low for insects and fruits, as dusk falls and then again at dawn. Their eyes can adapt to a wide range of illumination intensities, and even in extremely dim lights they can spot the tiniest movement of some unsuspecting prey.

Unlike most insect-hunters, they first catch their victims by snatching at them with their hands instead of biting directly at them. This is made possible by their 3-D vision, which enables them to judge distances in front of them with great accuracy, combined with their grasping fingers.

Related to the bush-baby is the slow loris, from Asia. This round-faced, pop-eyed character has a very similar way of life to the bush-baby's, but, as its name implies, it is much more leisurely about almost everything. It never leaps or jumps like its acrobatic relatives, but plods slowly and deliberately through the trees in search of its food. As it does not need to balance itself in mid-air, it has, during the course of evolution, lost its tail almost completely.

Its teeth are needle-sharp, and even a baby loris is quite prepared to bite the hand that feeds it. The loris is reputed to add a special delicacy to its diet in a most bizarre way by sneaking up on sleeping birds, gently strangling them and then eating their brains.

19

20

We are all familiar with the domestic guinea-pig, but few of us have made the acquaintance of its wild ancestor, the cavy (top left), or its relatives the agouti (centre left), the paca (below) and the capybara (opposite). They all come from South America, and the cavies there were first domesticated thousands of years ago by the Incas. The larger relations shown here have never been tamed to this extent. The long-legged agouti is too highly-strung and nervous, and the spotted paca is too shy . . .

21

. . . but the huge, semi-aquatic capybara often becomes very friendly indeed, as the pictures show, and it is surprising that this, the largest rodent alive today and probably the most intelligent, has never been developed as a domestic animal.

Some creatures owe their strangeness to the fact that they remind us of a familiar animal friend, but are oddly off-key in some indefinable way. The bush dog and the raccoon dog are dogs, certainly, but are somehow not quite 'right'.

The picture of the little bush dog from South America, showing the animal in a typical canine collar and chain, leaves you with an uneasy feeling. This feeling goes if you place your hand over its head. It then becomes simply an unidentified breed of dog. But as soon as you take your hand away and can see the long neck, the long sloping forehead, the small eyes and the rounded ears set far back, it becomes once again an animal oddity.

The raccoon dog is even more peculiar, and here the picture cannot be made more dog-like by covering over the head alone. The whole animal has become raccoon-like in both markings and proportions. And yet, with its typical canine feet and its posture, there is no mistaking that this is a true member of the dog family. The raccoon dog comes from the coldest and most remote areas of Asia and is the only member of its family that is known to hibernate.

Two creatures that are known to be closely related to the raccoon are the coatimundi and the kinkajou. The coati, from South America, which is shown on this page, is very similar indeed to the familiar 'coon' but has a much longer snout and bigger, more dangerous teeth. Always alert and always investigating the world around it, the coati moves about in gangs, working over areas of ground for any likely prey or other object of food.

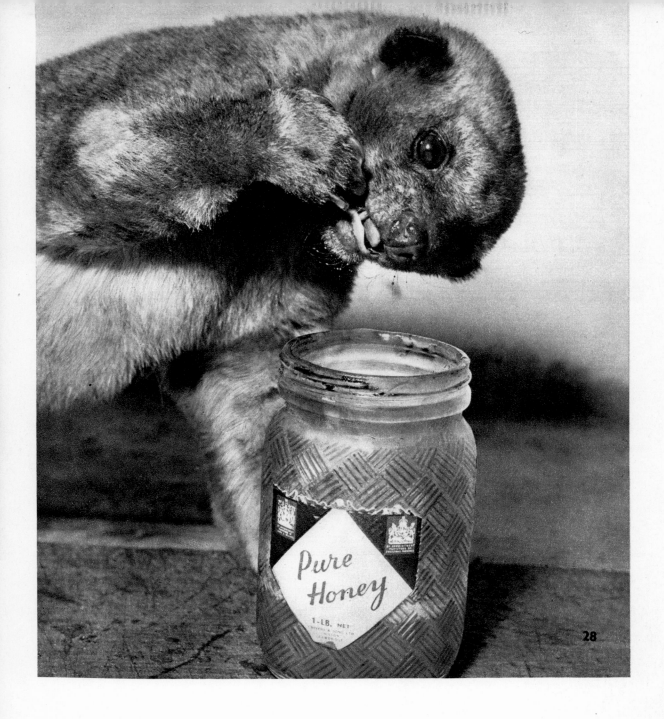

28

The kinkajou, found in South and Central America, is more monkey-like in appearance than the coati and, although a carnivore, has switched over to a much more varied diet which includes fruits, nuts, leaves, fungi, insects and, especially, honey, as well as small animals. Their passion for honey has led to their being given the inaccurate name of 'honey-bear' in America.

There are very few animals that are odd because of their posture, but the sloth is just such a creature. It is one of the few animals in the world that spends virtually its whole lifetime upside down. Its feet have become four powerful hooks, and during the day it crawls about in a leisurely manner high up in the trees of the South American forests. There it can find an ample food supply of leaves and fruits. It is particularly well camouflaged by virtue of the fact that a dense algal growth often develops on its coat, making the animal a bright green colour. In this way, it blends in perfectly with the rest of its forest home.

At the London Zoo one sloth developed a strange relationship with a little douroucouli. This small primate of South and Central America was allowed to sit, and even sleep, on its large companion. The benefit to the douroucouli was obvious enough, the sloth providing it with a soft, warm bed; but the reason for the sloth's behaving in such a tolerant way only became clear when it was realised that this is the way females of this species carry their young in the wild. The London Zoo's sloth—a female—was in fact 'mothering' the little primate, in the absence of a family of her own.

Some animals are striking, not because of one exaggerated feature, such as a huge nose, a long tail, bulging eyes or big ears, but because they bear a set of weird markings on an otherwise nondescript body. Such a creature is the Malayan tapir. The surface of the adult is boldly divided into three areas. The front and back regions are black and are separated by a bold white patch.

At first it is difficult to imagine how this arrangement of black and white markings can help the tapir in any way. But this is a creature that lives in dense forests, near water, and which is active at dawn and dusk. As the animal moves stealthily about in this broken half-light, it is possible that the markings break up the body into smaller areas and act as a kind of camouflage system.

The markings of young tapirs are even more striking. The spots and stripes of the Malayan tapir (above) and the South American tapir (below) at an early age are more typical of the camouflage patterns we find in forest dwellers.

34

The African wart-hog has often been called the ugliest animal in the world. Fond as one may become of it, it is difficult to defend the looks of an animal that has a wrinkled bristly skin, a straggling dishevelled crest, small baggy eyes, wickedly curved tusks, a huge warty head, a thick stubby neck and a heavy body on short stumpy legs. Add to this the fact that, when feeding, it bends its front legs under it and falls to its knees, and, when alarmed, it runs along with its tail held stiffly erect like a flagpole, and you will agree that the wart-hog can easily find a place of honour amongst the ranks of the animal oddities.

35

36

Looking like a shipwrecked Martian, this rare proboscis monkey was sighted swimming in the sea off the coast of its native Borneo. It was already two miles off shore and was heading straight out into the China Sea. When offered a sack trailed in the water, it clambered up into the boat and sat there in a state of near exhaustion, with its long tail dragging in the sea.

When the boat turned towards the land, the monkey sat quietly resting on the seat and was sufficiently recovered to jump back into the sea and swim the last hundred yards to the shore. Once on dry land, its huge, almost man-sized, form quickly disappeared into the forest. This was a rare encounter indeed, for proboscis monkeys have never been found 'at sea' before or since, have hardly ever been kept in captivity because of their delicate feeding habits, and are particularly shy in their native forest homes.

40

Dormice have nothing to do with doors. Their name is derived from the French *dormir* meaning 'to sleep', and it is their habit of spending the cold winter months in a deep sleep, waking only to eat from time to time, that has made them famous.

In the autumn they store up fat in their bodies and also lay in a good supply of food in their special winter nests. Then they curl their tails over their heads and go to sleep for the duration of the cold weather, waking again in the spring.

The coypu, a native of South America, is a very odd-looking aquatic rodent that has the misfortune to possess a coat of fur which is so wonderfully thick and dense that it appeals to the more barbaric members of that deadly predator, *Homo sapiens*.

The soft underfur of the coypu's coat is known as nutria in the fur trade, and on fur farms a number of colour variants have been developed, including the rare white one shown here.

The ring-tailed lemur is one of a group of primates that are found only on the island of Madagascar. The striking black and white rings marking the tail of this lemur are matched by other bold markings in the different species, and in some cases many colour forms may occur even within a single species. The lemurs have longer, more pointed, noses than their relatives, the monkeys, and their noises consist predominantly of gruntings, rather than chatterings.

45

Some of the lemurs, like this rare Crossley's dwarf lemur, are nocturnal. These night-active forms tend to be smaller and to have duller coats, without any special markings.

If there is one animal that can be described as the oddest creature alive today, it is without doubt the duck-billed platypus, found in Australia and Tasmania. With a duck-like beak, an otter-like body, a beaver-like tail and egg-laying behaviour like a reptile, this is surely the weirdest of mammals.

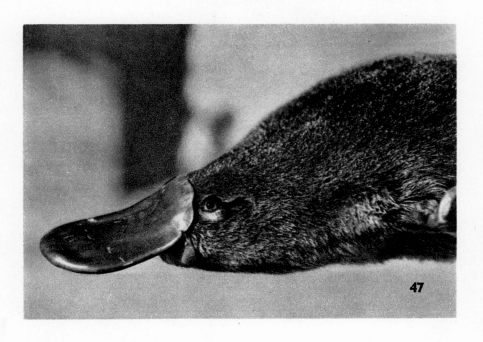

In addition to these strange features, the platypus possesses special poison glands on its hind legs. By jabbing at an enemy with two sharp spurs, one on each ankle, the platypus can inject its venom with painful efficiency. These poison spurs, present only in the males, are unique amongst mammals.

49

The hornbills of Africa and Asia have evolved an extreme form of self-protection. The female lays her eggs in a cavity in a tree and then proceeds to wall herself up inside the nest-hole. Using droppings and mud brought by her mate, she blocks up the entrance to the nest until there is only a narrow slit left. Through this the male must feed her during the weeks of incubation. While she is sitting on the eggs, the female undergoes a complete moult and eventually emerges in bright new plumage, her old feathers having formed the nest lining for the young birds. In this way, the hornbills manage to rear their young in safety, out of the clutches of marauding monkeys, squirrels or snakes.

The toucanet from Mexico is one of the smallest members of the gay and gaudy family of toucans that dwell in the forests of Central and South America. The huge beaks of the various toucans are usually brightly coloured, with special patterns. Apparently these markings act rather like flags, identifying the different species and serving as a form of social recognition. The great length of the beaks is related to the fruit-gathering habits of the birds, and in this respect the toucans are similar to the hornbills of the Old World.

No matter how familiar it becomes, the pelican, with its enormous pouched bill and its heavy squat body, still remains one of the oddities of the bird world. Its whole form has become modified in connection with its extreme specialisation as an enormous fish-trap.

Pelicans hunt in bands, moving over the water together until they have cornered a shoal of fish. Then, all at once, the whole group plunges forwards, the bills open and the great pouches fill with water and fish. Coming up again, the water draining away, the pelicans gobble down their catch—and lucky indeed is the fish that has escaped the onslaught.

The emu is a five-foot-tall bird from Australia that is curious in both senses of the word. It is an oddity because it belongs to the small group of large flightless birds that still exist today as remnants of a bygone era. Its living relatives are the ostrich, the kiwi, the rhea and the cassowary. It is also curious in the sense that it is inquisitive and will come padding up to a human being or any other strange object and peer cautiously at it with its huge dark eyes. Unfortunately, the fact that it lacks shyness, combined with its preference for grasslands, has made it an enemy of farmers, and in many areas this fascinating bird, with its beautifully striped young, has been completely exterminated.

56

A giant bird with a bony helmet is the cassowary from Australia and New Guinea. Its head is protected by this helmet when it rushes, plunging and crashing, through the thick undergrowth of the dense forests where it lives. It is one of the few living birds that can kill a man with ease. It attacks by leaping feet first at its enemy and striking downwards with its huge legs. In this way it has been known to rip open and slay people with a single blow.

The largest flying bird in the world today is the grotesque but majestic condor from the Andes, with a wing span of twelve feet. As with its relatives the vultures, its head and neck are naked and its face is submerged in a mass of folds, flaps, wrinkles and fleshy wattles.

60

When it comes to big mouths, the spoonbill, the shoebill and the frogmouth have few rivals. The impressive beak seen on the Old-World spoonbill (above) is a special filtering device used by the birds when feeding on small crustaceans in shallow water.

The shoebill, a relative of both storks and herons, inhabits the marches of the Nile, where it specialises in killing young crocodiles, terrapins, fish and frogs. Its vast, powerful beak, a deadly weapon when hunting, makes it perhaps the ugliest of all birds.

The frogmouth, found in Asia and Australia, is reported to catch insects, its sole source of nourishment, by opening its mouth wide and sitting quite still. The inner surface of its mouth is pink and yellow, whereas it body is camouflaged, and it is said to give the ill-fated insects the impression that this gaping cavity is really a brightly coloured flower. Attracted to it, they are quickly gobbled up.

Many of the oddities of the bird world have unusually big beaks, but with the quetzal (left) and the cock-of-the-rock (below) the beaks are nearly hidden from sight by the exaggerated crown feathers. The Central American quetzal is a curious bird, with unusually delicate plumage. The feathers fall out if the bird is even lightly handled, and their colours fade rapidly—a rare thing amongst birds.

The cock-of-the-rock, a native of South America, has a permanently erected crest that practically conceals its small beak. This strange bird's chief claim to fame lies in its extraordinary ritual dancing ceremonies. During these performances, one male at a time cavorts and postures on a rock or outcrop whilst the other males and the females watch near by.

Many birds have evolved large crests of feathers that are striking adornments when seen from the side, but some birds, like the South American harpy eagle shown below and the Old-World great crested grebe on the opposite page, have feather exaggerations around the whole face. These ruffs, which can be fluffed out when the birds are excited, give their owners an impressive appearance when seen head-on. Both these curious birds are professional killers, the grebe hunting fish and the eagle hunting monkeys.

Two birds with long, pointed beaks are the giant heron (above) and the tiny sun-bird (opposite). But here the resemblance ends. The heron's beak is used in conjunction with its long muscular neck, to spear the fish that are this bird's staple diet. But the little sun-bird is no killer. Its long, thin, curved bill has evolved in connection with its habit of sucking nectar from the tropical flowers of its native Africa. Its tongue is narrow and tube-like and can be used like a straw to suck the liquid from the flower into the bird's mouth. The sun-birds—there are over a hundred different kinds—are the African counterparts of the even smaller South American humming-birds.

The iguanas of South America are large frilled lizards with the spiky outlines that we have come to associate more with the reptilian monsters of fiction than with present-day creatures of fact. These six-foot-long tree-dwellers, with their jagged silhouettes, are members of a large family of lizards found throughout North and South America.

One of the seven hundred relatives of the iguana is the little horned toad of the North American deserts. This is not, of course, a true toad, but gets its name simply because it has a flattened, rounded toad-like shape to its stumpy body. This shape has evolved in connection with its habit of burying itself rapidly in the sand when hiding from its enemies.

The largest lizard alive in the world today, the Komodo dragon from the East Indies, reaches a length of ten feet and a weight of three hundred pounds. Its huge body, strong claws and long, flickering tongue certainly give it a dragon-like appearance and help to justify its rather dramatic name. But it is not always as fearsome as it looks, for, although it may attack and kill small deer and pigs in the wild, there was nevertheless one Komodo dragon at the London Zoo that became so tame that it was even known to give children rides on its back.

78

Many strange reptiles can enlarge themselves when angry or afraid. If alarmed, the bearded lizard from Australia increases the size of its head by distending its throat, thus spreading out around its lower jaw a savage fringe of sharp spines. Any enemy about to take a mouthful of bearded lizard can hardly be blamed for abandoning the exercise at this point.

79

At the London Zoo a bearded lizard shares a cage with a giant chameleon from Africa. If a disagreement occurs, the chameleon, too, can change its shape in a threatening manner. It flattens its body and, seen from the side, suddenly appears to be much larger than before. The two lizards also indulge in some angry colour changes, the chameleon blackening and the bearded lizard turning yellow and orange.

80

Tortoises have been stumping about the surface of the earth for literally hundreds of millions of years. The ancestors of our present-day tortoises found a successful formula for survival—a hard protective shell—and the family has remained much the same as it was almost at the dawn of the age of reptiles. Oddities today are the giant tortoises of the Seychelles and the Galapagos Islands. These monsters start out life, as the picture shows, looking rather like a common pet tortoise, but after fifty or a hundred years or so they grow to the vast weight of six hundred pounds, with shells measuring as much as fifty inches from end to end.

Whereas the giants of the tortoise world are harmless vegetarians, the much smaller snake-necked terrapin from the swamps of Australia is a deadly killer. Lashing out with its long neck, it grabs, kills and eats fish, frogs and even some water-birds.

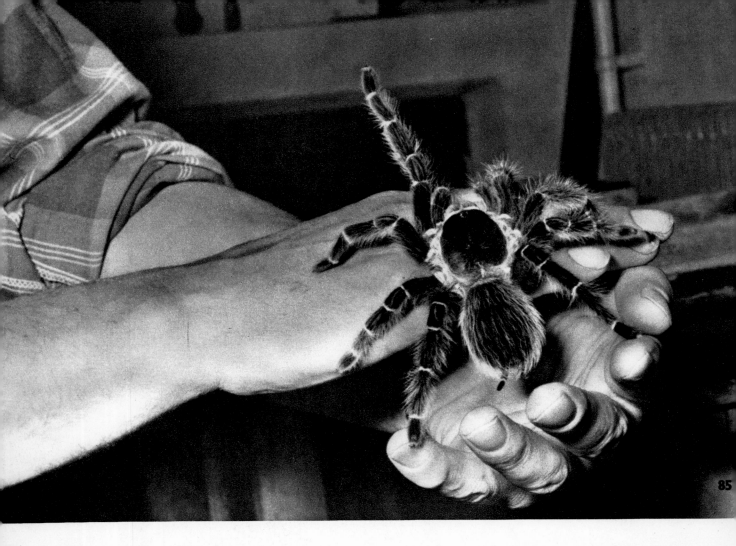

Many people find certain animals intensely repulsive. The bird-eating spider, from South America, comes into this category. But, in reality, the dreaded monster can become quite a pet, as the photograph shows. However, it can only be handled with safety by an expert who knows how to keep it calm, for, if unduly agitated, it has two very effective lines of defence. When mildly angry, it tears its hair out! The fine hairs on the abdomen are pulled out by the back legs and thrown in your face. They are stinging hairs and can be very painful. If this fails to work, the spider can deliver an extremely poisonous bite.

Less dangerous than the bird-eating spider are the various kinds of frogs. These, too, are considered by many people to be unspeakably unpleasant, principally, it seems, because of their slimy skins. But, if they are examined closely, both the tree-dwelling forms and the ground-living forms reveal many curious and intriguing features. The tree-frog (right), for example, with its huge eyes and long, bulbous-tipped fingers and toes, has a special form of egg-laying. The female scoops up mud at the water's edge to make a series of miniature puddles in which the eggs are laid, and, when they hatch, the young can swim about in comparative safety.

The enormously fat barking-toad (below) from Brazil, with its triangular spikes over the eyes and its complex camouflage markings, has, as its name suggests, a loud rasping cry which it emits when annoyed.

87

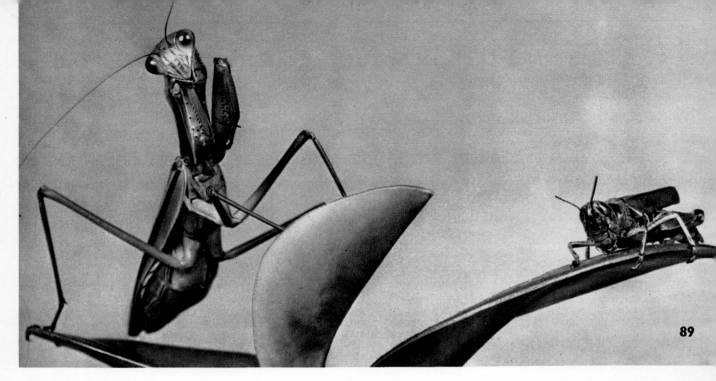

Of all the thousands of strange insects, the praying mantis is one of the most bizarre. Its chief claim to notoriety is the female's habit of eating the male immediately after mating. Sometimes she starts eating him while he is mating with her. In addition to this unsavoury behaviour, the mantis has a far from pleasant feeding pattern. It lies stealthily in wait for other insects, its enormously long and powerful front legs folded up in an attitude of pious prayer. When a victim approaches, these legs shoot out at terrific speed, grab the prey, hold it tight and press it back to the region of the mouth. The sharp spines on the mantis' front legs grip the victim firmly whilst the killer eats it alive.